VERS

UNIVERSE

A collection of poems for children

Published by BBC Educational Publishing,
a division of BBC Enterprises Limited,
Woodlands, 80 Wood Lane, London W12 0TT

First published 1992
© BBC Enterprises Limited 1992
Illustrations © 1990 Rob Chapman (pages 9, 15, 20, 24, 27, 30, 32,
33, 34, 38, 45, 46, 49, 50, 55, 57, 62, 66 and 69); Bethan Matthews
(pages 121, 122, 124, 126, 127, 129, 130, 131, 132, 133, 134 and 135);
Nick Price (pages 71, 73, 78, 79, 81, 84, 85, 86, 88, 90, 92, 93, 94, 95,
96, 104, 105, 108, 109, 110, 111, 116, 117, 119 and 120); Masud
Sheik (pages 69, 97 and 101).

Cover illustration © 1992 Mark Dobson
ISBN 0 563 34982 4

Contents

Introduction

I know a man who's so forgetful
that one night he put his cat to bed
and put himself outside.
                    Michael Rosen

Strange place this universe of ours, isn't it? For instance,
bits of it pass right through other bits of it all the time,
but they don't seem to care, or even to notice. (And bits
of it are flying through us, but we won't go into that . . .)
We're flying through the universe now, at thousands of
miles an hour, yet we seem to be standing up on our feet
perfectly still. But . . . 'miles an hour'? Hours shrink and
grow. 'Standing up'? We certainly don't know which way
is up.

Yes, it's a strange universe, and *Verse Universe* is stranger
still! Inside these covers there's a universe of poems – an
outside, a lightside, a darkside.

Roger McGough's wordfish search the oceans for an S.
Richard Edward's once-a-century worm appears for its
once-a-century breath. Gareth Owen's commentator
conveys the electric atmosphere as Danny Markey is
tackled by a drainpipe in an international football match.

Terry Jones' trousers walk away and leave him. Benjamin Zephaniah's teacher goes out with a frog he met in a bog. The terrible monster in one of Libby Houston's poems turns into an emperor with a shining cloak of silver. The Circus of Poets try collecting stamps … but no one sends them letters.

These poets have chosen for you some of their best poems, as well as poems they like by other writers. They all made their selections for the BBC School Radio series *Verse Universe*.

So, put the cat of your unimagination to bed and put yourself outside, between *these* covers, to tumble, stroll, float, dive, stand on your head through, under, round, on the dark side of, above, inside-out the *Verse Universe*.

John Tuckey
BBC Producer, *Verse Universe*

GARETH OWEN

Gareth Owen has published three books of poetry, three novels and several plays. As well as being a writer he's a man of the theatre, acting and directing. When invited, he works in schools, reading from his own work as well as suggesting ways for younger writers to begin and develop.

Gareth says writing is difficult – even for a professional writer. 'Starting a new piece of work is like standing in the middle of the desert and finding a signpost with arms pointing in five hundred different directions – and no names on the arms! Somehow you have to choose which way you'll go.' One piece of advice he gives to young writers is 'Always bear in mind the person or people you feel you're writing for – your audience. Without some idea of an audience, writing is pointless, and it always shows.'

Gareth now lives in the Welsh countryside where he has his own large garden, and says he gets quite excited these days at travelling to big cities.

BETWEEN THE GASWORKS
◆ AND THE CEMETERY ◆

Horror film

Well sir, first of all there was this monster
But like he's not really a monster
'Cause in real life he's a bank clerk sir
And sings in this village choir
But he keeps like drinking this potion sir
And you see him like changing into this pig
With black curly hairs on its knuckles;
And what he does sir,
Is he goes round eating people's brains.
Anyway before that sir, I should have said
He's secretly in love with Lady Irene
Who's very rich with lots of long frocks
And she has this identical twin sister
Who looks like her sir
Who keeps getting chased by this monster bulldog
Into these sinking sands
That's inhabited by this prehistoric squid sir
Which like she can't see
Because the deaf and dumb bailiff
With the hump on his back
Has trod on her specs.

Anyway before that sir,
I should have said,
This lady Irene is screaming,
'Henry, Henry, my beloved, save me,'
'Cause she's been walled up in the dripping dungeon
With the mad violinist of the vaults
By the manservant with the withered boot sir,
But this Henry, he can't hear her sir,
Because he's too busy
Putting people in this bubbling acid bath
To make them stay young forever sir
But his experiments keep going wrong.
Anyway, before that sir,
I should have said,
Her Dad can't rescue her either sir
Because of the army of giant ants
That's eating his castle;
And the music sir, it's going,
'Tarrar, tarrar, boom boom tarrar sir,'
And 'Henry, Henry my beloved,'
She keeps screaming
And the mad violinist of the vaults sir
He starts going funny all over the flagstones.
And like, Algernon sir,
No not him sir, the other one,
He can't do nothing about the squid in the bogs
Because he's turning into this pig with hairy knuckles.

Anyway before that sir, I should have said,
There's this huge mummy in the library
And every time he hears this music
Starts tearing off all these dirty bandages
And smashing through these walls and everything
And the professor can't stop him
'Cause he's gone off his rocker
And keeps bulging his eyes and laughing a lot
When suddenly this vampire…
Didn't I tell you about the vampire sir?
Anyway before that there's this vampire
Who's been dead for thousands of years
But he's a Swiss greengrocer in real life
But the iceberg his coffin's in
Gets all broken up sir
When it collides with Dr Strenkhoff's submarine sir,
That's carrying this secret cargo
Of radio active rats…
Didn't I tell you about the radio-active rats sir?
Well anyway sir
Before that I should have said…

Gareth Owen

First day at school

A millionbillionwillion miles from home
Waiting for the bell to go. (To go where?)
Why are they all so big, other children?
So noisy? So much at home they
must have been born in uniform.
Lived all their lives in playgrounds.
Spent the years inventing games
that don't let me in. Games
that are rough, that swallow you up.

And the railings
All around, the railings.
Are they to keep out wolves and monsters?
Things that carry off and eat children?
Things you don't take sweets from?
Perhaps they're to stop us getting out.
Running away from the lessins. Lessin.
What does a lessin look like?
Sounds small and slimy.
They keep them in glassrooms.
Whole rooms made out of glass. Imagine.

I wish I could remember my name.
Mummy said it would come in useful.
Like wellies. When there's puddles.
Yellowwellies. I wish she was here.
I think my name is sewn on somewhere.
Perhaps the teacher will read it for me.
Tea-cher. The one who makes the tea.

Roger McGough

Maths problems

Please add these up:
One ton of sawdust.
One ton of old newspaper.
Four tons of string.
One half-ton of fat.
Have you got all that in your head?
'Yes.'
I thought so.

Take any number.
Add ten.
Subtract three.
Now close your eyes.
(Your friend closes his eyes.)
Dark, isn't it!

Alvin Schwartz

14

Our school

I go to Weld Park Primary,
It's near the Underpass
And five blocks past the Cemetery
And two roads past the Gas
Works with the big tower that smells so bad
     me and me mates put our hankies over our
          faces and pretend we're being attacked
               by poison gas … and that.

There's this playground with lines for rounders,
And cricket stumps chalked on the wall,
And kids with their coats for goalposts
Booting a tennis ball
Around all over the place and shoutin' and arguin'
     about offside and they always kick it over
          the garden wall next door and she
               goes potty and tells our head teacher
                    and he gets right ratty with
                         everybody and stops us playin'
                              football…
                                   …and everything.

Gareth Owen

◆ SATURDAY GAME ◆

The commentator

Good afternoon and welcome
To this international
Between England and Holland
Which is being played here today
At 4, Florence Terrace.
And the pitch looks in superb condition
As Danny Markey, the England captain,
Puts England on the attack.
Straight away it's Markey
With a lovely little pass to Keegan,
Keegan back to Markey,
Markey in possession here
Jinking skilfully past the dustbins;
And a neat flick inside the cat there.
What a brilliant player this Markey is
And he's still only nine years old!
Markey to Francis,
Francis back to Markey,
Markey is through, he's through,
No, he's been tackled by the drainpipe;
But he's won the ball back brilliantly
And he's advancing on the Dutch keeper,
It must be a goal.

The keeper's off his line
But Markey chips him superbly
And it's a goal
No!
It's gone into Mrs Spence's next door.
And Markey's going round to ask for his ball back,
It could be the end of this international.
Now the door's opening
And yes, it's Mrs Spence,
Mrs Spence has come to the door.
Wait a minute
She's shaking her head, she is shaking her head,
She's not going to let England have their ball back.
What is the referee going to do?
Markey's coming back looking very dejected,
And he seems to be waiting…
He's going back,
Markey is going back for that ball!
What a brilliant and exciting move!
He waited until the front door was closed
And then went back for that ball.
And wait a minute,
He's found it, Markey has found that ball,
He has found that ball
And that's wonderful news
For the hundred thousand fans gathered here
Who are showing their appreciation
In no uncertain fashion.

But wait a minute,
The door's opening once more.
It's her, it's Mrs Spence
And she's waving her fist
And shouting something I can't quite understand
But I don't think it's encouragement.
And Markey's off,
He's jinked past her on the outside
Dodging this way and that
With Mrs Spence in hot pursuit.
And he's past her, he's through,
What skills this boy has!
But Mr Spence is there too,
Mr Spence in the sweeper role
With Rover their dog.
Markey's going to have to pull out all the stops now.
He's running straight at him,
And he's down, he's down on all fours!
What is he doing?
And Oh my goodness that was brilliant,
That was absolutely brilliant,
He's dived through Spence's legs;
But he's got him,
This rugged stopper has him by the coat
And Rover's barking in there too;
He'll never get out of this one.
But this is unbelievable!
He's got away

He has got away:
He wriggled out of his coat
And left part of his trousers with Rover.
This boy is real dynamite.
He's over the wall
He's clear
They'll never catch him now.
He's down the yard and on his way
And I don't think we're going to see
Any more of Markey
Until it's safe to come home.

Gareth Owen

You tell me

Here are the football results:
League Division Fun
Manchester United won, Manchester City lost.
Crystal Palace 2, Buckingham Palace 1
Millwall Leeds nowhere
Wolves 8 A cheese roll and had a cup of tea 2
Aldershot 3 Buffalo Bill shot 2
Evertonill, Liverpool's not very well either
Newcastle's Heaven Sunderland's a very nice place 2
Ipswhich one? You tell me.

Michael Rosen

Saturdays

Real
Genuine
Saturdays
Like marbles
Conkers
Sweet new potatoes
Have their especial season
Are all morning
With midday at five o'clock.

True Saturdays
Are borrowed from early Winter
And the left overs
Of Autumn sunshine days
But separate from days of snow.
The skies dine on dwindles of smoke
Where leafy plots smoulder
With small fires.
Sunday meat is bought
And late
Large, white loaves
From little corner shops.
People passing
Wave over garden walls,
Greengrocers and milkmen are smiled upon
And duly paid.
It is time for the chequered tablecloth
And bowls of soup.
And early on
We set out with some purpose
Through only
Lovely Saturday,
Under skies
Like sun-shot water,
For the leccy train
And the Match in Liverpool

Gareth Owen

Saturday afternoon

And it's humming,
A hum comes from the bowl.
And the people inside seem to be saying,
Come in, come on in,
And you jostle at the turnstile,
And the turnstile clicks and clicks,
And you push nearer and nearer,
Through the dark gap,
Then you're in.
And the great stand of the City end,
It's like a hall,
A great hall,
And you go on,
Through the arch
And you see the pitch,
Green, new shaven and watered,
And the groundsman's made the white lines,
As straight as a ruler,
And the ash is pressed.
And you find your place among the fans,
The real fans,
The singers and chanters and rattle wavers.
And a sheet of tobacco smoke hangs over the crowd.
And the crowd whistles and hoots,
And the policemen circling the pitch
Look up and know they're in for a rough day of it,

And the stadium fills up,
The Open End first, then the City End,
Then the paddock, then the covered seated stand,
Then last of all, the fat directors
With the Lord Mayor and cigars.
And the reporters are in their little glass box,
And the cameramen position themselves
By the goal,
And there's a looking down the tunnel,
Then a hush.
Then out they come.
The lads.
Like toy footballers on a green billiard table.
And a roar goes up...

  City, City, City, City,
  We'll support you evermore,
  We'll support you evermore.
  City, City, City, City,
  We'll support you evermore,
  We'll support you evermore.

Peter Terson (from *Zigger Zagger*)

Tich Miller

Tich Miller wore glasses
with elastoplast-pink frames
and had one foot three sizes larger than the other.

When they picked teams for outdoor games
she and I were always the last two
left standing by the wire-mesh fence.

We avoided one another's eyes,
stooping, perhaps, to re-tie a shoelace,
or affecting interest in the flight

of some fortunate bird, and pretended
not to hear the urgent conference:
'Have Tubby!' 'No, no, have Tich!'

Usually they chose me, the lesser dud,
and she lolloped, unselected,
to the back of the other team.

At eleven we went to different schools.
In time I learned to get my own back,
sneering at hockey-players who couldn't spell.

Tich died when she was twelve.

Wendy Cope

24

Playing with Fred

I lie on my bunk bed
Trying to sleep.
The night closes around me
Like an envelope black.
Underneath me
Plays Dominic
My little brother.
I tell him,
'Be quiet! Get into bed!'
But he just shouts back,
'I'm playing with Fred.'

It's like this always.
At dinner time
Dominic will say,
'Get off Fred
You're sitting on him.
Get out of the way.'
'Shutup you Dodo!'
I say in reply.

One Summer's day
We were all bathing
When:
'Help Fred's drowning!'
We heard a cry.
So my father swam out
To rescue him.

When he hit the shore
Dominic wailed,
'That's not Fred!
That's Ted, his brother.'

Well, you would never believe
How many we went through.
All his relations
And all his friends
Until at last Dom cried,
'Yes, that's him.'

Puffing and blowing
My dad sat down.
'You just can't win,'
He wearily said
As he sat down on the sand
And slept.

Adam Goddard

Sally won't you walk with me?

'Sally won't you walk with me
Walking heel and toe
Sally can we secrets share
As home from school we go.'

Arm in arm by lane and hedge
So many tales to tell
And every tale breeds tales anew
As we walk in a magic spell.

'And do you know what Brenda said
And how Alan banged his head
How Antonia cried at dinner time
And what Jemima said?'

'And wasn't dinner awful?
And Sally tell your dream
And will you come to tea next week?
And isn't Rose a scream?'

'Did you really tell your mother that
Did your sister cut your hair
Did you see that lady on the bike
Did you see those two boys stare?'

'And Sally look, stop giggling
Oh Sally honestly
Oh Sally don't you pull that face
Those people there will see.'

'What did your father say to that
And did you do it again?
You didn't really, I don't believe!
Sally what happened then?'

We whisper over Sally's gate
Till her mother calls her to tea
So many secrets still to tell
So many tales about me.

And if I could wish my days again
If time were a golden spool
I'd wish I could walk for ever
With Sally home from school.

Gareth Owen

The leader

I wanna be the leader
I wanna be the leader
Can I be the leader?
Can I? I can?
Promise? Promise?
Yippee, I'm the leader
I'm the leader

OK what shall we do?

Roger McGough

The quarrel

I quarrelled with my brother
I don't know what about,
One thing led to another
And somehow we fell out.
The start of it was slight,
The end of it was strong,
He said he was right,
I knew he was wrong!

We hated one another.
The afternoon turned black.
Then suddenly my brother
Thumped me on the back,
And said, 'Oh, *come* along!
We can't go on all night –
I was in the wrong.'
So he was in the right.

Eleanor Farjeon

RICHARD EDWARDS

Richard Edwards started writing poems at school and he can't stop. He writes in shiny red notebooks – the kind with a wire spiral down the side. He doesn't usually get ideas out of the blue like bolts of surprise lightning. He sits down with his pen at the ready and scribbles words and phrases and lines until a good idea comes through. Then he works on it and hopes it will turn itself into a poem good enough to keep. As well as writing, he sometimes teaches English to foreign students as a way of making a living. He has lived in France and Italy but is back in England at the moment.

He has published six books of poems: *The Word Party* and *Whispers from a Wardrobe* (Puffin); *A Mouse in My Roof, Phoots!* and *The Giant Claydelbaydel* (Orchard Books); and *If Only...* (Viking Kestrel).

I WANT YOU TO GET UP
◆ OUT OF YOUR SEAT ◆

maggie and milly and molly and may
went down to the beach (to play one day)

and maggie discovered a shell that sang
so sweetly she couldn't remember her troubles, and

milly befriended a stranded star
whose rays five languid fingers were;

and molly was chased by a horrible thing
which raced sideways while blowing bubbles: and

may came home with a smooth round stone
as small as a world and as large as alone.

for whatever we lose (like a you or a me)
it's always ourselves we find in the sea

e e cummings

Walking out

Bored with people telling her
Which clothes she ought to wear,
Which colours would be flattering,
Which way to cut her hair,

Bored with worrying how to lose
A sag, an inch, a stone,
She took her body off one day
And walked out in her bone.

It wasn't cold. The warm breeze buffed
Her spine until it shone,
She skipped a bit – how free it felt
To be a skeleton!

She crossed a field: friendly moos
From kind unstartled cattle,
They waved their tails, she waved her hands –
Rattle, rattle, rattle.

She crossed a wood: brambles raked
Her shins but did no harm,
A song-thrush and a lazy robin
Hitched lifts on her arm.

She crossed a bridge and stopped to watch
Her image on the river,
An eel wove between her ribs
Making her shadow shiver.

She reached the shore. Whispering waves
Ran up. Would they support her?
She crossed the sea, she crossed the sea:
Bone on the water.

Richard Edwards

33

To pass the time

When I'm bored I count things:
Cornflakes, cars,
Pencils, people, leaves on trees,
Raindrops, stars,
Footsteps, heartbeats, pebbles, waves,
Gaggles, herds and flocks,
Freckles, blinks per minute,
The ticks
Of clocks.

Eighty-seven lamp-posts
Line our street.
Did you know a woodlouse has
Fourteen feet?
And – three vests, four pairs of pants, six shirts, two
T-shirts, one pair of jeans, two other pairs of trousers,
one pair of shorts, two belts, three pullovers (one of them
without sleeves), a raincoat, a jacket, two pairs of pyjamas,
one glove, one tie and eleven socks are
The clothes I've got
In five drawers and one wardrobe:
I'm bored
A lot.

Richard Edwards

The nose

The nose went away by itself
in the early morning
while its owner was asleep.
It walked along the road
sniffing at everything.

It thought: I have a personality of my own.
Why should I be attached to a body?
I haven't been allowed to flower.
So much of me has been wasted.

And it felt wholly free.
It almost began to dance.
The world was so full of scents
it had had no time to notice,

35

when it was attached to a face
weeping, being blown,
catching all sorts of germs
and changing colour.

But now it was quite at ease
bowling merrily along
like a hoop or a wheel,
a factory packed with scent.

And all would have been well
but that, round about evening,
having no eyes for guides,
it staggered into the path
of a mouth, and it was gobbled
rapidly like a sausage
and chewed by great sour teeth –
and that was how it died.

Ian Crichton Smith

Taking my pen for a walk

Tonight I took the leash off my pen.
At first it was frightened,
looked up at me with confused eyes, tongue panting.
Then I said, 'Go on, run away,'
and pushed its head.
Still it wasn't sure what I wanted;
it whimpered with its tail between its legs.
So I yelled, 'You're free, why don't you run –
you stupid pen, you should be glad.
Now get out of my sight.'
It took a few steps.
I stamped my foot and threw a stone.
Suddenly, it realised what I was saying
and began to run furiously away from me.

Julie O'Callaghan

WATCHING ME
◆ WATCHING YOU ◆

Phizzog

This face you got,
This here phizzog you carry around,
You never picked it out for yourself, at all, at all, – did you?
This here phizzog – somebody handed it to you – am I right?
Somebody said, 'Here's yours, now go see what you can do
with it.'
Somebody slipped it to you and it was like a package
marked:
'No goods exchanged after being taken away' –
This face you got.

Carl Sandburg

Big Bert

Big Bert sat on a cushion,
'I'm much too fat,' moaned he,
'Who else could be so miserable?'
The cushion answered: 'Me!'

Richard Edwards

The window

She looks in through the window
And wonders who they are –
The woman in the green silk dress,
The man with a cigar,
The black cat on the rocking-chair,
The girl in bows and lace,
The boy who sees her looking in
And pulls a funny face.

She steps back from the window
And rubs her eyes and blinks –
But no one's lived in this old house
For years and years, she thinks;
And when she looks again the room
Is dark and cold and bare,
Just brick-ends, shadows, spiders
And a broken rocking chair.

Richard Edwards

38

Green man in the garden

Green man in the garden
   Staring from the tree,
Why do you look so long and hard
   Through the pane at me?

Your eyes are dark as holly,
   Of sycamore your horns,
Your bones are made of elder-branch,
   Your teeth are made of thorns.

Your hat is made of ivy-leaf,
   Of bark your dancing shoes,
And evergreen and green and green
   Your jacket and shirt and trews.

Leave your house and leave your land
   And throw away the key,
And never look behind, he creaked,
   And come and live with me.

I bolted up the window,
   I bolted up the door,
I drew the blind that I should find
   The green man never more.

39

But when I softly turned the stair
　　As I went up to bed,
I saw the green man standing there.
　　Sleep well, my friend, he said.

Charles Causley

Face to face

I looked into the mirror,
I looked and scratched my head,
The face that goggled back at me
Was not my face, instead
It was a leering monkey's
Staring a cheeky stare –
All yellow teeth and flapping ears,
All wrinkles, folds and hair.

'Clear off, you rude imposter,
Back to some jungly place,
When I look in my mirror I
Expect to see my face,
A human one, and humans
Are not like you!' I cried.
'Well, that shows how much you know, chum,'
The grinning ape replied.

Richard Edwards

40

The Once-a-Century Worm

A quiet wood, a scratching sound from underneath a bush,
I ran to look; the leaf-mould quaked, then gave an upward
   push
And, gaping as it surfaced in that dim and shady place,
A worm emerged, a worm that wore a tiny human face.

'I am the Once-A-Century Worm,' it squeaked, 'and we are
   rare,
For only every hundred years we need a gulp of air,
And when we've gulped that gulp we disappear back
   underground
To doze and dream before another century comes round.'

With that it closed its eyes and stretched its little worm-mouth
   wide,
Breathed in until a century's worth of air was safe inside,
And then sank out of sight, while in its place a worm-cast
   curled –
But what's a common worm-cast to convince this doubting
   world?

So now I take a camera with me everywhere I go
And crawl around on hands and knees beneath the bushes,
   so
If I should see another one, a photo will confirm
The strange (but true) existence of the Once-A Century Worm.

Richard Edwards

41

Some one

Some one came knocking
At my wee, small door;
Some one came knocking,
I'm sure – sure – sure;
I listened, I opened,
I looked to left and right,
But nought there was a-stirring
In the still dark night;
Only the busy beetle
Tap-tapping in the wall,
Only from the forest
The screech-owl's call,
Only the cricket whistling
While the dewdrops fall,
So I know not who came knocking,
At all, at all, at all.

Walter De La Mare

42

Two of a kind

I stalk the timberland,
I wreck and splinter through,
I smash log cabins,
I wrestle grizzly bears.
At lunch time if I'm dry
I drain a lake or two,
I send the wolves and wolverines
Howling to their lairs.
I'm Sasquatch
Bigfoot
Call me what you like,
But if you're a backpacker
On a forest hike,
Keep a watch behind you,
I'm there, though rarely seen.
I'm Bigfoot,
Sasquatch,
I'm mean, mean, mean.

I rear up from the waves,
I thresh, I wallow,
My seven snaky humps
Leave an eerie wake.
I crunch the silly salmon
Twenty at one swallow,
I tease the silly snoopers –
A fiend? A fish? A fake?

I'm the Monster
Nessie
Call me what you please,
But if you're a camper
In the lochside trees,
Before you zip your tent at night
Say your prayers and kneel.
I'm Nessie,
The Monster,
I'm real, real, real.

Richard Edwards

Chinese giant

Poor Zeng Qin Lian.
She is the tallest woman in the world.
She is only sixteen and her father's head
is at her elbow.
Her bones ache when she stands –
she uses her family's shoulders for crutches.
She bends down every morning
to look at herself in the mirror.
It is not easy for her in China
where there is such an absence of height.
The neighbours point her out to visitors
as she is the only local landmark.
Her father noticed how difficult it was
for her to eat with normal chopsticks –
like slurping soup with a teaspoon.
He carved her a special set
as big as two candlesticks.
Now her six bowls of rice at lunch and dinner
don't take her so long to polish off.
I am sorry for you, Zeng Qin Lian.

Julie O'Callaghan

45

Nameless

Where are you going, man in grey,
Shabby and sad on this bright blue day?

– I'm looking for my name.

Why do you search along the gutter,
Poke through dustbins, moan and mutter?

– I'm looking for my name.

Why do your fingers trace each mark
Carved on trees and benches in the park?

– I'm looking for my name.

Why do you study trails in the grass,
The secret words of frost on glass?

– I'm looking for my name.

Where are you going, man in grey,
Shaking your head as you walk away?

– I'm looking for my name. I'm looking for my name.

Richard Edwards

Who's that?

Who's that
stopping at
my door in the
dark, deep
in the dead of the moonless night?

Who's
that in the quiet
blackness,
darker than dark?

Who
turns the han-
dle of my door, who
turns the old brass hand-
le of
my door with never a sound, the handle
that always
creaks and rattles and
squeaks but
now
turns
without a sound, slowly
slowly
        slowly
                round?

Who's that moving through the floor
as if it were a lake, an open door? Who
is it who passes through
what can never be passed through,
who passes through
the rocking-chair
without rocking it,
who passes through
the table without knocking it, who
   walks out of the cupboard without unlocking it?
Who's that? Who plays with my toys
with no noise, no
noise?

Who's that? Who is it
silent and silver
as things in mirrors, who's
as slow as feathers,
shy as the shivers,
light as a fly?

Who's that who's that
as close as
close as a hug, a kiss—

Who's THIS?

James Kirkup

ROGER McGOUGH

Some writers have more than one job, but Roger McGough spends all his time writing poems and performing them. He works with live audiences as well as on radio and television, has made hit records as part of 'The Scaffold' and has published a lot of books, including *Nailing the Shadow*, *Sky in the Pie* and *The Imaginary Menagerie*. Roger was born in Liverpool, went to University in Hull and now lives in London. As he says in *Nailing the Shadow*:

The best thing
about being famous

is when you walk
down the street

and people turn round
to look at you

and bump into things

THE MYSTERIOUS
◆ WORDFISH SHOW ◆

Hide and seek

When I played as a kid
How I longed to be caught
But whenever I hid
Nobody sought

Roger McGough

Ever see
an oyster
in a cloister?

Then how about
a monkfish?

Roger McGough

Lies

When we are bored
My friend and I
Tell
Lies.

It's a competition: the prize
Is won by the one
Whose lies
Are the bigger size.

We really do:
That's true.
But there isn't a prize:
That's lies.

Kit Wright

Nothingmas Day

It was Nothingmas Eve and all the children in Notown were not tingling with excitement as they lay unawake in their heaps.

D
  o
    w
      n
        s
          t
            a
              i
                r
s their parents were busily not placing the last crackermugs, glimmerslips and sweetlumps on the Nothingmas Tree.

Hey! But what was that invisible trail of chummy sparks or vaulting stars across the sky
    Father Nothingmas – drawn by 18 or 21 rainmaidens!
    Father Nothingmas – his sackbut bulging with air!
    Father Nothingmas – was not on his way!
(From the streets of the snowless town came the quiet of unsung carols and the merry silence of the steeple bell.)

Next morning the children did not fountain out of bed with cries of WHOOPERATION! They picked up their Nothingmas Stockings and with traditional quiperamas such as: 'Look what I haven't got! It's just what I didn't want!' pulled their stockings on their ordinary legs.

For breakfast they ate – breakfast.

After woods they all avoided the Nothingmas Tree, where Daddy, his face failing to beam like a leaky torch, was not distributing gemgames, sodaguns, golly-trolleys, jars of humdrums and packets of slubberated croakers.

Off, off, off went the children to school, soaking each other with no howls of 'Merry Nothingmas and a Happy No Year!', and not pulping each other with no-balls.

At school Miss Whatnot taught them how to write No Thank You Letters.

Home they burrowed for Nothingmas Dinner.
The table was not groaning under all manner of
   NO TURKERY
   NO SPICED HAM
   NO SPROUTS
   NO CRANBERRY JELLYSAUCE
   NO NOT NOWT
There was not one (1) shoot of glee as the Nothingmas Pudding, unlit, was not brought in. Mince pies were not available, nor was there any demand for them.

Then, as another Nothingmas clobbered to a close, they all haggled off to bed where they slept happily never after.

   and that is not the end of the story......

Adrian Mitchell

53

Wordfish
are swordfish
in a state of undress

Criss-crossing
the ocean
in search of an S.

Roger McGough

To amuse
    emus
on warm summer nights

    Kiwis
do wiwis
from spectacular heights.

Roger McGough

Fire guard

My wife bought a fire-guard for the living room.

Seems a nice sort of chap.

Roger McGough

Pet Food

What do you get, Jude,
When you eat Pet Food?

Hamsterburgers,
Poodle Pies,
Goldfish Fingers,
Canary Fries.

Budgie Bangers,
Dachshunds and Mash,
Pickled Parrots,
Corned Cat Hash.

Gerbils on Toast,
Tortoise Teas,
Horse-in-a-basket,
Mice and Peas.

That's what you get, Jude,
When you eat Pet Food!

Terry Jones

All's well that ends

Peter was awake as soon as daylight sidled into his bedroom. Saturday at last. He jumped out of bed and flung open the curtains. Thank goodness, he thought, not a cloud in the sky. As he gazed out of the window, he wondered about the day ahead. Would his school team win the county cricket trophy? (*No.*) Would he score his first century? (*No, l.b.w. second ball.*) Would Helen be at the party in the evening? (*Yes.*) Would she let him dance with her, walk her home and kiss her? (*No, she'd spend all night smooching and snogging with O'Leary.*)
Would the police discover Grandma's body behind the woodshed? (*Yes, on Monday.*) And if so, would they think it was an accident? (*No, sorry.*) Or suicide? (*Hardly.*) Would he be incarcerated? (*What's that?*) Put in prison (*Yes.*)

But during his time inside, wouldn't he determine to make amends, study hard and gain early parole? Wouldn't he find a steady job and settle down? One day meet a decent girl and raise a family? Eventually, wouldn't he own a national chain of DIY supermarkets, give money to charity, become a model citizen respected and loved by the whole community? Say yes (*No.*)
But surely all's well that ends? (*Well . . . . .*

Roger McGough

56

DOGS TO LET (AND OTHER
◆ 4-LEGGED POEMS) ◆

I used to keep
   a blue macaw
in my bedside
   bottom drawer

But he was never
   happy there
among my socks
   and underwear

He pined for sunshine
   trees galore
as in Brazil
   and Ecuador

Knowing then
   what I must do
I journeyed south
   as far as Kew

In the Gardens
   set him free
(wasn't that macaw-
   ful of me?)

Roger McGough

The Fly

The Fly
Is the Sanitary Inspector. He detects every speck
With his Geiger counter.
Detects it, then inspects it
Through his multiple spectacles. You see him everywhere
Bent over his microscope.
He costs nothing, needs no special attention,
Just gets on with the job, totting up the dirt.

All he needs is a lick of sugar
Maybe a dab of meat –
Which is fuel for his apparatus.
We never miss what he asks for. He can manage
With so little you can't even tell
Whether he's taken it.

In his black boiler suit, with his gas-mask,
His oxygen pack,
His crampons,
He can get anywhere, explore any wreckage,
Find the lost –

Whatever dies – just leave it to him.
He'll move in
With his team of gentle undertakers,
In their pneumatic protective clothing, afraid of nothing,
Little white Michelin men,
They hoover up the rot, the stink, and the goo.

He'll leave you the bones and the feathers – souvenirs
Dry-clean as dead sticks in the summer dust.

Panicky people misunderstand him –
Blitz at him with nerve-gas puff-guns,
Blot him up with swatters.

He knows he gets filthy.
He knows his job is dangerous, wading in the drains
Under cows' tails, in pigs' eye-corners
And between the leaky broken toes
Of the farm buildings.
He too has to cope with the microbes.
He too wishes he had some other job.

But this is his duty.
Just let him be. Let him rest on the wall there,
Scrubbing the back of his neck. This is his rest-minute.

Once he's clean, he's a gem.

A freshly barbered sultan, royally armoured
In dusky rainbow metals.

A knight on a dark horse.

Ted Hughes

Pets

Pets are a godsend to people who enjoy the company of
small animals. Cats, for example, are very popular.
As are dogs. We had a dog once called Rover, but he
died. So now we don't call him anything.

Roger McGough

A catapillow
is a useful pet

To keep
upon your bed

Each night you simply
fluff him up

Then rest
your weary head.

Roger McGough

The flea is small
And no one's pet
But likes to hear
Of Dogs to Let

Max Fatchen

60

Nursery rhyme

What do we use to wash our hair?
We use shampoo to wash our hair.
It's tested scientifically for damage to the eyes
by scientists who, in such matters, are acknowledged to be wise.
Shampoo. Wash hair. Nice, clean habit.
Go to sleep now, darling.
It doesn't hurt the rabbit.

What makes lather in the bathtub?
Soap makes lather in the bathtub.
Rub-a-dub till bubbles bob along the rubber ducks race!
But don't get any in your mouth because soap has a nasty taste.
Bath time. Slippy soap! Can't quite grab it!
Let's get dried now, darling.
It doesn't hurt the rabbit.

61

What makes us better when we're ill?
Medicine helps us when we're ill.
Years of research helped to develop every pill you take,
Like that one we gave you when you had a tummy ache.
Cut knee. Antiseptic. Gently dab it.
Kiss you better, darling.
It doesn't hurt the rabbit.
It doesn't hurt
It doesn't hurt
It doesn't hurt the rabbit.

Carol Ann Duffy

Bookworms
  are the cleverest
of all the worms I know

While others
  meet their fate
on a fisherman's hook as bait

Or churn out silk
  or chew up earth
or simply burn and glow

They loll
  about in libraries
eating words to make them grow

62

(Vegetarians mainly,
  they are careful
what they eat

Avoiding names
  of animals
or references to meat)

They live
  to ripe old ages
and when it's time to wend

They slip
  between the pages
curl up, and eat 'The End'.

Roger McGough

PROCEED WITH CARE –
◆ FAMILY AHEAD ◆

Uncle Roger

I am distinctly
ununclely.
I forget birthdays
and give Xmas presents
only when cornered.
(Money, of course, and too little.)

I am regrettably
ununclish.
Too thin to be jolly,
I can never remember
jokes or riddles.
Even fluff
my own poems.

My nephews and nieces
as far as I know
disuncled
me some time ago.
Better uncleless
than my brand of petty
uncleness.

Roger McGough

Bossy Parrot (my sister)

Mum said, PIANO! Emma,
  Bossy Parrot said, Mum said piano!

Mum said, BATH! Emma,
  Bossy Parrot said, Mum said bath!

Mum said, SUPPER! Emma,
  Bossy Parrot said, Mum said supper!

That does it, I said.

Homework!! Move your blazer!
Move your bag!
My sister is a Bossy Parrot!!!

Emma Reid (aged 9)

64

Anteater

Anteater, Anteater
Where have you been?
Aunt Liz took you walkies
And hasn't been seen.

Nor has Aunt Mary
Aunt Flo or Aunt Di.
Anteater, Anteater
Why the gleam in your eye?

Roger McGough

Listn big brodda dread, na!

My sista is younga than me.
My sista outsmart five-foot three.
My sista is own car repairer
and yu nah catch me doin judo with her.

> I sey I wohn get a complex.
> I wohn get a complex.
> Then I see the muscles my sista flex.

My sista is tops at disco dance.
My sista is well into self-reliance.
My sista plays guitar and drums
and wahn see her knock back double rums.

> I sey I wohn get a complex.
> I wohn get a complex.
> Then I see the muscles my sista flex.

My sista doesn mind smears of grease and dirt.
My sista'll reduce yu with sheer muscle hurt.
My sista says no guy goin keep her phone-bound—
with own car mi sista is a wheel-hound.

> I sey I wohn get a complex.
> I wohn get a complex.
> Then I see the muscles my sista flex.

James Berry

Grandad

Grandad's dead
And I'm sorry about that.

He'd a huge black overcoat.
He felt proud in it.
You could have hidden
A football crowd in it.
Far too big –
It was a lousy fit
But Grandad didn't
Mind a bit.
He wore it all winter
with a squashed black hat.

Now he's dead
And I'm sorry about that.

66

He'd got twelve stories
I'd heard every one of them
Hundreds of times
But that was the fun of them:
You knew what was coming
So you could join in.
He'd got big hands
And brown, grooved skin
And when he laughed
It knocked you flat.

Now he's dead
And I'm sorry about that.

Kit Wright

67

The Unincredible Hulk-in-law

Being the Incredible Hulk's
scrawny stepbrother ain't easy.
Sticky-fisted toddlers
pick fights with me
in misadventure playgrounds.

On beaches
seven-stone weaklings
kick sand in my eyes
vandalize my pies
and thrash me with candyfloss.

They all tell their friends
how they licked the Hulk...
(...well not the Hulk exactly,
but an incredibly unincredible relative).

Bullied by Brownies
mugged by nuns
without a doubt
the fun's gone out
of having a T.V. star in the family.

Think I'll marry
Wonderwoman's asthmatic second cousin
and start a commune in Arkansas
for out-of-work, weedy
super heroes-in-law.

Roger McGough

68

MICHAEL ROSEN

Michael Rosen is a poet, performer, broadcaster and scriptwriter. He was educated at 'Tyne Holme Nursery School and Wadham College, Oxford'.

He worked for three years at the BBC but has been writing for children since 1970. He has produced over 16 books for children. He has also won the Signal Poetry Award.

Michael Rosen lives in East London with his wife and five children.

A trip to Morrow

I started on a journey just about a week ago
For the little town of Morrow in the State of Ohio.
I never was a traveller and really didn't know
That Morrow had been ridiculed a century or so.
I went down to the depot for my ticket and applied
For tips regarding Morrow, interviewed the station guide.
Said I to he, 'My friend, I want to go to Morrow and return
Not later than to-morrow, for I haven't time to burn.'

Said he to me, 'Now let me see, if I have heard you right,
You want to go to Morrow and come back to-morrow
    night,
You should have gone to Morrow yesterday and back
    to-day,
For if you started yesterday to Morrow, don't you see
You should have got to Morrow and returned to-day at
    three.
The train that started yesterday, now understand me right,
To-day it gets to Morrow and returns to-morrow night.'

Anon

Lost

In a terrible fog I once lost my way,
Where I had wandered I could not say,
I found a signpost just by a fence,
But I could not read it, the fog was so dense.
Slowly but surely, frightened to roam,
I climbed up the post for my nearest way home,
Striking a match I turned cold and faint,
These were the words on it, 'Mind the wet paint.'

James Godden

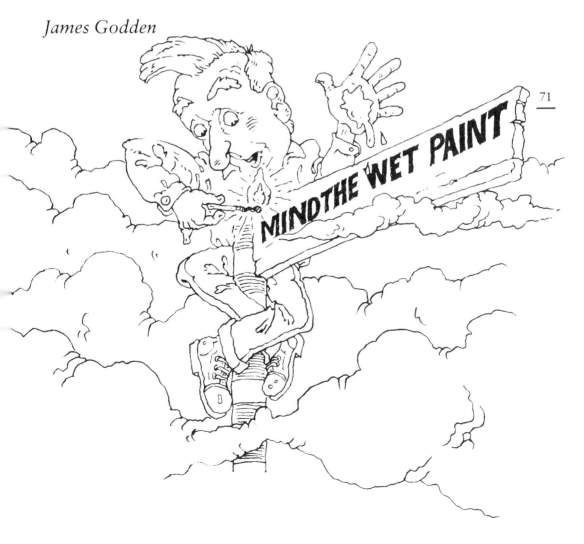

See you later, alligator.
In a while, crocodile.
See you later, hot potato.
If you wish, jelly-fish.
Not too soon, you big baboon.
Toodle-oo, kangeroo.
Bye-bye, butterfly.
See you tomorrow, horror.
In a week, freak.

Anon

72

Boasts

I know a man who's so good at jumping
that he can jump across a river
and back
without touching the other side

The streets are so narrow round here
that the dogs wag their tails up and down

It's so windy round here
you go out
you get blown against the wall and flattened out as wafers
they peel you off the walls
and sell you off as circus posters

There's a man round here
who is so tall
he has to climb a ladder to shave himself
when he was born he was so big
it was impossible to name all of him at once
he grew so fast
his head grew three inches through the top of his hat

I know two fellows
who are lazy
it takes two of them to chop wood
one swings the axe
the other grunts

I know a man who's so forgetful
that one night he put his cat to bed
and put himself outside

Collected from various sources by Michael Rosen

73

The Skyfoogle

There was a man
who turned up round our way once
put up a tent in the park, he did,
put up notices all round the streets saying
that he was going to put on show
A TERRIFYING CREATURE!!!!!!
called:
THE SKYFOOGLE!!!!!!!
No one had ever seen this thing before.
The show was on for
2 o'clock, the next day.

Next day, we all turned up to see
THE FIERCEST ANIMAL IN THE WORLD!!!!!!!!
The man took money at the door.
And we poured in the tent.
There was a kind of stage up one end
with a curtain in front of it.
We all sat down and waited.
The man went off behind the curtain.
Suddenly we heard a terrible scream.
There was an awful yelling and crying,
There was the noise of chains rattling
and someone shouting.
Suddenly the man came running on to the stage
in front of the curtain.

All his clothes were torn,
there was blood on his face
and he screamed:
Quick, get out
get out
get out of here,
THE SKYFOOGLE HAS ESCAPED!!!!!!!

We got up
and ran to the door
and got away as fast as we could.

By the time we got ourselves together
the man had gone.
We never saw him again.
We never saw our money again either…
…And none of us has ever seen THE SKYFOOGLE!!!!!

Traditional, adapted by Michael Rosen

Dopey and Dozey

Dopey's wife sent him down town
to fetch a bucket of ice.
He came back with a pail of water
'I got this half price
because it was melted.'

Dopey and Dozey were in jail.
They were trying to find a way out
'I know,' says Dopey
'I'll shine my torch up to that window
you crawl up the beam of light
and open up that window.'
Dozey didn't like the sound of that.
'I know you, Dopey,
I'd get halfway up the beam
and you'd turn the light off.'

Adapted from a variety of sources by Michael Rosen

76

My old man's a dustman

My old man's a dustman
he wears a dustman's hat
he bought two thousand tickets
to see a football match

Fatty passed to Skinny
Skinny passed it back
Fatty took a rotten shot
and knocked the goalie flat.

Where was the goalie
when the ball was in the net?
Half way up the goalpost
with his trousers round his neck.

Singing:
umpah umpah
stick it up your jumper
rule Britannia
marmalade and jam
we threw sausages at our old man.

They put him on the stretcher
they put him on the bed
they rubbed his belly
with a five pound jelly
but the poor old soul was dead.

Anon

◆ AT HOME ◆

My brother's on the floor roaring
my brother's on the floor roaring
why is my brother on the floor roaring?
My brother is on the floor roaring
because he's supposed to finish his beans
before he has his pudding.

But he doesn't want to finish his beans
before he has his pudding.

He says he wants his pudding
NOW

but they won't let him

so now my brother is on the floor roaring.

They're saying
I give you one more chance to finish those beans
or you don't go to Tony's
but he's not listening
because he's on the floor roaring

he's getting told off
I'm not
I've eaten my beans
do you know what I'm doing now?
I'm eating my pudding
and he's on the floor roaring.

If he wasn't on the floor roaring
he'd see me eating my pudding
and if he looks really close
he might see a little tiny smile
just at the corner of my mouth.
But he's not looking.
He's on the floor roaring.

79

The pudding is OK.
It's not wonderful
not wonderful enough
to be sitting on the floor and roaring about –
unless you're my brother.

Michael Rosen

Irritating sayings

Isn't it time you thought about bed?

It must be somewhere

You speak to him Harold, he won't listen to me

Who do you think I am?

You'd better ask your father

It's late enough as it is

Don't eat with your mouth open

In this day and age

Did anybody ask your opinion

I remember when I was a boy

And after all we do for you

You're not talking to your school friends now you know

Why don't you do it the proper way

I'm only trying to tell you

What did I just say?

Now, wrap up warm

B.E.D. spells bed

Sit up straight and don't gobble your food

For the hundredth time

Don't let me ever see you do that again

Have you made your bed?

Can't you look further than your nose?

No more lip

Have you done your homework?

Because I say so

Don't come those fancy ways here
Any more and you'll be in bed
My, haven't you grown
Some day I won't be here, then you'll see
A chair's for sitting on
You shouldn't need telling at your age
Want, want, want, that's all you ever say

Collated by David Jackson

My mum said

My mum said to me and my brother:
'Don't crumble your bread or roll in the soup.'
I said:
'I don't want to roll in my soup.'

Then she said:
'Eat up, Michael.'
And my brother said:
'I don't want to eat up Michael.'

Michael Rosen

81

All for an ice-cream

'Mum, can I have an ice-cream?'

'Go ask your dad.'

'Dad, can I have an ice-cream?'

'Go ask your mum.'

'But I've just asked her and she told me to ask you.'

'Well tell her that I've just told you to ask her.'

'Mum, dad's just told me to tell you that you've got to tell me if I can have an ice.'

'Oh well I suppose you can but ask your dad for 10p.'

'Right.'

'Dad, can I have 10p for an ice-cream?'

'I haven't got 10p.'

'Oh come on dad you haven't looked yet and oh hurry the van'll go soon.'

'Let's have a look then, ah, there you are.'

'Thanks dad, Ohh!'

'What's the matter now?'

'The van's gone.'

Karen Jackson

82

Auntie and uncle

My auntie gives me a colouring book and crayons.
I begin to colour.
After a while she looks over to see what I have done and
    says
you've gone over the lines
that's what you've done.
What do yo think they're there for, ay?
Some kind of statement is it?
Going to be a rebel are we?
I begin to cry.
My uncle gives me a hanky and some blank paper
do your own designs he says
I begin to colour.
When I have done this he looks over and tells me they are all
    very good.
He is lying,
only some of them are.

John Hegley

Bed!

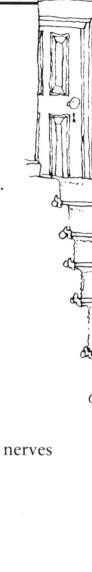

When it is time to go to bed
my mum says:
'Bed!'
I say:
'Please can I stay up
until this film finishes?'
'What time does it finish?' my mum says.
'Ten o'clock,' I say.
'No way,' my mum says.
'Oh can't I stay up for five minutes?'
'NO.'
'Please.'
'NO!'
'Oh…can't I read in bed?'
'NO!'
'Please.'
'Come here, girl…You're getting on my nerves
if you're not in that bed
by the time I count to…'

I walk slowly up the stairs
my brother is laughing away.
Then my mum starts shouting again.
This time at my brother.

Joni Akinrele

84

When Betty eats spaghetti

When Betty eats spaghetti,
She slurps, she slurps, she slurps.
And when she's finished slurping,
She burps, she burps, she burps.

Colin West

If I was a bird...

If I was a bird
I would like to fly in the sky
so that everyone could see me.
I could fly in and out of the clouds and caves.
There'd be just one pest in my life –
that's a man with a gun to shoot me.
Him I wouldn't like.

If I was a man and not a bird,
I'd never shoot at birds
because a bird is lovely to see
when it's flying.
If I was a man I'd just watch,
not shoot.

Anon

86

Tidy your room

They say
Tidy your room –
But I'm trying to kill a fly on the wall
with a rolled-up comic.

They say
I'm asking you to tidy your room –
but I'm trying to kill the fly
by squashing it with a chunk of plasticine.

They say,
I am now TELLING you to tidy your room –
and I'm rolling up bits of plasticine.

For the last time – TIDY YOUR ROOM
but I'm making a line of the rolled-up bits of plasticine
along the edge of the chair.

They say,
Can you hear me?
I say, Yes.
I'm now flicking the bits of plasticine
at the fly on the wall.
They say,
What have we just asked you to do?
And I say,
I don't know.

Michael Rosen

87

No one in

Sometimes you come home
and there's no one in.
There are no lights on
no food ready
no telly
no one laughing
no jokes
just you
on your own.

That's when my brain
starts doing things:
you know,
murderers and mad dogs stuff.

I'll tell you what I do.
When I open the door
I shove it really hard and fast
and it bangs against the wall
really loud
so if he's hiding behind the door
he'll get it right on the nose.

I never have got him
I'll tell you what did happen though.
The door handle
made a great big hole in the wall.

Michael Rosen

88

Minnie

I went downtown
To meet Mrs Brown.
She gave me a nickel
To buy me a pickle.
The pickle was sour
She gave me a flower
The flower was dead
She gave me a thread
The thread was thin
She gave me a pin
The pin was sharp
She gave me a harp
The harp began to sing
Minnie and a minnie and a ha, ha, ha.
Minnie and a minnie and a ha, ha, ha,
Kissed her fellow in a trolley car.
I told Ma, Ma told Pa.
Minnie got a licking and a ha, ha, ha.

Anon (USA)

What's its name?

Between my nose and upper lip
There runs a cleft; a trough; a slip;
A runnel; furrow; gutter; split;
I wish I knew the name for it.

Willard R. Espy

The cupboard

I was in the dark cupboard
all alone
sitting on the washing basket.
I switched the torch on
and I put my shadowed hand
on the ceiling.
My hand was so big
it was nearly as big as the cupboard.

Kevin Wright
Rushcroft School, Walthamstow

a heavy rap

i can run faster than any gazelle
last time i had a race i left him
on the inside corner of the indy 500
i can outswim any ole fish
gave a dolphin a half-hour start
and still beat him across the ocean
i mean i'm so bad i gave a falcon
a half-mile lead and beat him to the top of the mountain
i roared so loud the lion hung his head
in shame and his wife came and asked me to
please
leave that part of the jungle as her husband's
feelings
were so hurt by my together thing
i had jumping contest with a kangeroo and
jumped clear outa australia and passed the
astronauts
on their way back down
i can rap so hard Rap Brown hates to be
in the same town with me
and i'm only ten
this year coming

Nikki Giovanni

I hate and I love

I hate and I love. And if you ask me how,
I do not know: I only feel it, and I'm torn in two.

Catullus
Traditional

Nightmare

I never say his name aloud
and don't tell anybody
I always close all the drawers
and look behind the door before I go to bed
I cross my toes and count to eight
and turn the pillow over three times
Still he comes sometimes
one two three
like a shot
glaring at me with his eyes,
grating with his nails
and sneering his big sneer –
the Scratch Man

Oh-oh, now I said his name!
Mama, I can't sleep!

Siv Widerberg

92

When I was small

When I was small
the wall was tall.
But now I'm tall
the wall looks small.

Jay Reed
John Scorr School

My paper route

When 3.30 or 4 o'clock comes around
It's like fresh roses
Because it's time to deliver my papers

It feels so good to meet my customers
and say hello
And then say goodbye

I deliver 81 papers during the week
So I hear 81 hellos
And 81 goodbyes

And 109 on Saturday.

Troy Vacciano

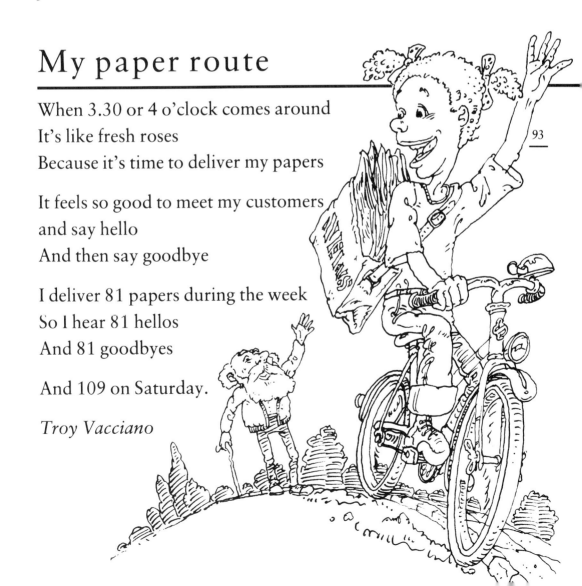

93

Why?

When the vase gets broken, why do I always get the blame?
When the garden's untidy, why do I have to clear it up?
When the book gets ripped, why do I have to mend it?
When someone breaks the pencil lead, why do I get the
　　blame?
When the newspaper gets lost, why do I have to find it
　　again?

I can answer all these questions.

Because I broke the vase
Because I made the garden untidy
Because I ripped the book
Because I broke the pencil lead
Because I lost the paper.

Ben Bruton
Wood's Foundation C of E School

94

Wasps

Wasps like coffee.
Syrup.
Tea.
Coca-Cola.
Butter.
Me.

Dorothy Aldis

96

BENJAMIN ZEPHANIAH

Benjamin was born in Birmingham in 1958. He spent his early years in Jamaica and the life and people of the island have been a strong influence on his work. His poems have what he calls 'wordability' – the gift of using words to maximum effect, creating vivid pictures and ideas. For *Verse Universe*, Benjamin has written a play in the dub style. What's dub? Have a look at the start of the play which we've printed overleaf, have a listen to it on *Verse Universe* and above all – enjoy!

OUR TEACHER'S GONE
◆ CRAZY ◆

SILLY BILLY: Good morning students

ALL: Good morning teacher

SILLY BILLY: Now you should have a lesson
But it doesn't matter
Today you will listen to me as I rap
and I will welcome any backchat
Yes today my students you will learn about
me
I am always acting normal but today I'll be
silly
My real name is Silly Billy and I come from
Billaricky
I used to be a hippy and I love to take the
mickey
I like to play with spiders and they like to
play with me
When everyone's asleep at night I play with
my budgie
My budgie speaks good English and speaks
Portuguese
And I have a cat called Cat who has some
lovely fleas

I like to ride my pushbike with my mouth
    open wide
Just in case a fly or something wants to go
    inside
I love all animals my girlfriend is a frog
We're happy together, I met her in a bog.

1ST FEMALE: Our teacher's gone crazy

1ST MALE: Our teacher's gone mad

SILLY BILLY: You must get to know me better, lessons will
    be fun
I know you will feel better for it once the
    lesson's done
Forget about the workings of the world and
    let's get happy
Forget the mysteries of the past and let's go
    party
I am not going crazy, I am just being myself
Cause everyday that I come here I feel like
    someone else
I wanna have some fun today, I am letting
    myself go

1ST MALE: That's the way to do it Sir

SILLY BILLY: I got to let you know, yes I love school
        dinners
and I like my custard cold,
I don't like detention or doing as I'm told
I am in love with Primrose Hill, I can't
        control my thought
I like football and hockey but I can't stand
        wearing shorts

1ST FEMALE: Oh Sir what has come over you?

SILLY BILLY: I just want to be cool
I wanna be like Michael Jackson

1ST MALE: Sir – go back to school.

THE CIRCUS OF POETS

Martyn Wiley Ian McMillan John Turner David Harmer

THE CIRCUS OF POETS first got together in 1981 following chance meetings between Ian, Martyn and John. The idea formed to write and present the kind of poems that are fun to perform and fun to hear. Their work reflects the natural rhythm that occurs in everyday language and they've shouted and chanted their way through dozens of broadcasts, hundreds of live shows and one supermarket entrance (to an audience of a Japanese tourist and a pneumatic drill).

The CIRCUS write their poems to be performed and the 'scripts' that they use actually split the lines up between the different members of the group, as in the script for a play. In the poems that we've printed, we've taken out the 'who says what' but you might like to try splitting up the lines between a group of friends and so turn a 'reading poem' into a performing poem.

All of the CIRCUS also follow careers as solo writers and often visit schools.

MUM SAYS I NEED
◆ A HOBBY ◆

No good at hobbies

I'm no good at hobbies me
I'm no good at all
I've tried every one there is
I've flipping tried them all

I tried to join the boy scouts
tied me in knots

I tried the Brownies
wouldn't let me in

Tried the Boys Brigade
didn't have a bugle

Tried the Sea Cadets
no boat

I'm no good at hobbies me
I'm no good at all
I've tried every one there is
I've flipping tried them all

I tried collecting seashells
I live in Birmingham

I tried collecting stamps
I don't get any letters

I tried collecting bubble gum wrappers
I hate bubblegum

I tried collecting train numbers
they closed the line

I'm no good at hobbies me
I'm no good at all
I've tried every one there is
I've flipping tried them all

I tried astronomy
it was cloudy

I tried playing the piano
we haven't got one

I tried fishing
I fell asleep

I tried roller skating
on ice

I'm no good at hobbies me
I'm no good at all
I've tried every one there is
I've flipping tried them all

But I'll tell you what I am good at
Not much

Hobby-horse

I've got a hobby,
It's a hobby-horse.
Not a doggy
Or a moggy,
But a horse of course.
Don't go jogging,
Or hob-nobbing,
Just go riding
On my Dobbin.
Want a hobby?
Get a hobby
Get a hobby-horse.

I've got a hobby,
It's a hobby-horse.
See that whippet,
I can lick it
On my hobby-horse.
Faster than a bullet,
Goes as fast as I can pull it.
Want a hobby?
Get a hobby
Get a hobby-horse.

104

I've got a hobby,
It's a hobby-horse.
See that cheetah,
I can beat her
On my hobby-horse.
I'll ride from Lands End to Dover,
Though I usually fall over.
It's not easy
Skin my knees-y
On my hobby-horse.

I've got a hobby,
It's a hobby-horse.
Don't knock it –
Like a rocket,
Is my hobby-horse.
A steed for the choosy,
Though it wears out the shoes-y.
Hear the news-y,
Lose the blues-y.
Get a hobby-horse.

Is it a bird?
Is it an aeroplane?
No –
It's a hobby
It's a hobby
It's a hobby-horse.

SO WHAT ARE WE GOING TO ◆ DO THIS SATURDAY? ◆

Disco

1-2-3-4
Who's that knocking on my door?
5-6-7-8
Birthday party, don't be late
For the disco disco disco dancing
Disco disco disco dancing

Jellies, ice-cream, crisps and popcorn,
Fizzy fizzy drinks and paper hats.
Musical chairs, pass the parcel,
Nearly all my friends are here, that's
Darren, Julie, Tracy, Ben and
Rachel, Jason, Emma and Paul.
Laughing, singing, disco dancing.
Suddenly, no lights at all.

Dad shouted 'It's a power cut'.
No music, no party.
Mum yelled out 'Don't be scared'.
No music, no party.
Jason started crying, sat on the jelly.
No music, no party.
Emma started laughing, burst a balloon.

No music, no party.
Let's light the candles on my cake.
No music, no party.
Darren groaned 'I feel sick'.
No music, no party.
I felt around, my cake had vanished.
No music, no party.
All of a sudden, the lights came on.

Jellies, ice-cream, crisps and popcorn,
Fizzy fizzy drinks and paper hats.
Musical chairs, pass the parcel,
Nearly all my friends are here, that's
Darren, Julie, Tracy, Ben and
Rachel, Jason, Emma and Paul.
Laughing, singing, disco dancing
Joining in now that we're all
Disco disco disco dancing
Disco disco disco dance.

In our car

In our car
In our car
In our c-c-car.
In our car
In our car
In our brand new car.

We're up, we're away – it's a beautiful day,
Zooming along on the motorway.
Dad at the wheel, picnic in the boot,
Sunshine and laughter, planning the route.

In our car
In our car
In our c-c-car.
In our car
In our car
In our brand new car.

Crunch, bang – what's that?
Crunch, bang – what's that?
A whistle and a knock, a thumping shock,
A whining fizz and a crack on the block.
A rattle and a splutter and a groaning mutter
Cuts through the racket like a knife through butter.

That's our car
That's our car
That's our c-c- sshhhhhhhhhhh…
That's our car
That's our car
That's our c-c- sshhhhhhhhhhh…

Crunch, bang – what's that?
Crunch, bang – what's that?
A shove and a kick, dad's got a stick.
And he's banging on the engine cos it makes him sick.
A mallet and a crow-bar to try and make it go far.
He'd be better off trying to drive my granny's sofa.

We've stopped, we're stuck – we're out of luck,
Waiting for the man with the breakdown truck.
Out with the picnic, up with the bonnet.
We'll be here for hours, bet your life upon it.

In our car
In our car
In our c-c-car.
In our car
In our car
In our useless car.

109

Going to the panto

We went to a panto
Oh no you didn't
Oh yes we did
We went to a panto
Oh no you didn't
Oh yes we did

All about a lad called Aladdin
And his Uncle Abanazer, now he was a bad'un
Aladdin's in his cave, cold and damp
So he gives a rub of a funny little lamp
Up pops a genie in a cloud of smoke
Gives him three wishes then chokes for a joke.

Oh no he didn't
Oh yes he did
Oh no he didn't
Oh yes he did.

He's behind you, he's behind you
Look out Aladdin, he's behind you.

Aladdin's old mum was a bloke in a dress
Throwing custard pies about blimey what a mess
Aladdin got rich, had to wear a crown
Locked up his uncle coz his trousers fell down
Married a princess, lived happily ever after
I cried with laughter and the story got dafter.

Oh no you didn't
Oh yes I did
Oh no you didn't
Oh yes I did

He's behind you, he's behind you
Look out Aladdin, he's behind you.

We went to a panto
Oh no you didn't
We did!

OH NO, IT'S MORE
◆ SCHOOL TRIPS ◆

At the castle

In twos we go
There's me and my mate
There's two in front
And two behind.

And teacher says
We've got to be good.
We haven't got to mess
About or run around
And we mustn't throw our
Sandwich wrappings
Off the battlements.

Because there's not just us
Visiting the castle
This morning.
There are other
Members of the public too,
Whatever they are.

In twos we go
There's me and my mate
There's two in front
And two behind.

And teacher says
I don't need to wear my batman mask.
There's very little crime
Inside ruined castles.
But I'll keep my eyes open,
Just in case.

And I mustn't throw my
Tennis ball
Against the walls.
Teacher says that's probably
How the place got ruined
In the first place.
But I didn't think
The Normans played tennis.

113

In twos we go
There's me and my mate
There's two in front
And two behind.

And teacher says
I mustn't play marbles
With my mate
On top of the walls
They might roll off
And hit
Other members of the public,
Whatever they are.

They'd be lucky
If they'd be hanging around
Under the walls in
The days when the castle was built,
They wouldn't get hit with marbles.
It'd be boiling oil
And arrows.
Teacher says that's different,
Members of the public,
Whatever they are,
Don't try and storm the castle these days,
They pay to come in.
Teacher laughs.
I don't see the joke myself.

114

In twos we go
There's me and my mate
There's two in front
And two behind.

I'm sitting in the coach
With the driver.
I'm in disgrace.
My marbles have been confiscated.
The driver's reading The Sun.
He says he hates children.
And teachers.

I'm supposed to write about this
When we get back to school.
She'd better give me my marbles back
First.

TRIPS

For our school trip this term
we're going to Mars

It's £1.50
We're taking sandwiches
and a flask.

We might be back late at night
but as long as the driver gets it right
we won't splash down off Scarborough.

I'd rather go to the zoo
There isn't much to do on Mars.

Next term
we're going to the sun.

It's £3.00
We're taking swimming trunks
and dark glasses

We'll be camping overnight
and as long as the driver gets it right
we won't splash down off Scarborough.

I'd rather go to the zoo
I've seen the sun before.

116

Poems can do almost anything their poets want them to do, and many of them tell stories.

The two poems here show that poems can tell very different stories.

Terry Jones' 'The revolt of the clothes' starts with the perfectly commonplace event of a shirt yawning, stretching and walking off, but goes on to tell of matters that could be a threat to civilization as we know it.

'Francesco de la Vega', by Charles Causley, is a long poem and only part of it is printed here. It's a strange, eerie story of a boy who cut himself off from people all together and became a creature of the sea. He did not even learn to speak, except one word – the name of his village. Perhaps the strangest and eeriest thing about the story is that it's said to be true.

The revolt of the clothes

My shirt was sitting next to me
One sweltering Summer's day
When suddenly it yawned, got up,
Then stretched, and walked away!

Well, I didn't really mind that.
I thought: perhaps it's just a game,
When bless me! moments later –
My trousers did the same!

'I say!' I said (quite loudly)
And I jumped up to my feet,
And I ran after those trousers
As they tore off down the street.

But they just went like the clappers
(With no legs to slow them down)
And they dashed across the High Street,
And then off and out of town.

Well I didn't stop to ponder,
I just chased them through the dirt,
Over hills they leapt and bounded
Till they caught up with my shirt.

And the two of them kept going
Till they reached a certain wood,
Where they disappeared together.
I thought: 'Now they've gone for good.'

Well I almost gave up hope then,
But I quickly changed my mind,
When I found my trouser buttons
And my braces left behind.

So I followed through a thicket,
Till I heard a curious sound
Like a hundred windy wash-days
Flapping lightly on the ground.

Then I peered into a clearing,
And could not believe my eyes,
For there a million trousers danced
Of every shape and size.

120

And a million shirts and blouses,
Sun-hats, socks and dungarees,
Dresses, cardigans and jackets,
And some clothes one seldom sees!

There were suits and skirts and bodices,
And those things you wear to ski,
Alongside woollies, whites and winter wraps,
All happy to be free.

Francesco de la Vega

Francesco de la Vega
From the hours of childhood
Passed his days
In the salt of the ocean.

Only one word he spoke.
Lierjanes! – the name
Of the sea-village of his birth
In the Year of God 1657.

While other children
Helped in field or kitchen,
Wandered the mountain-slope,
He swam the wild bay.

While others were at church
He dived to where lobster and squid
Lodged in the sea's dark cellar.
He must suffer a salt death, said Father Ramiro.

His mother and father entreated him
To come to his own bed.
His brothers and sisters called him
Home from the yellow sand-bar.

Amazed, they watched him
Arrow the waves like a young dolphin.
Until they tired of waiting, he hid
Under the mountain of black water.

Libby Houston has spent thirty years so far finding out where being a poet leads. Her first ambition was to be an explorer, but this territory – poetry – has turned out strange enough . . . She began by reading her work to audiences and has given performances all over Britain, besides running poetry workshops for adults and children. She has published four books of poetry.

Her own children are grown up now. She lives in Bristol and works as a rock-climbing botanist, counting the flowers on the cliffs of the Avon Gorge.

◆ INSIDE AND OUT ◆

Like a maze

One day, just after Christmas, we went to the Sales.
My sister wanted a dark blue tracksuit,
my mum was going for vests and curtains,
coats for us, boots – next year's presents!
And anything good, she said, going cheap at the big store.

We pushed in through the glass door.

'Follow us, now. Don't get lost.'
Follow-my-leader, my
mum's red coat led
twist and turn through a jostling jungle
of coats, arms, bags, backs, thick and thin,
deeper and deeper in –

And then she stopped.
She reached in a tray.
I looked away –
and there through a gap, just for a moment,
I saw a row of little fur dogs on a table,
and one of them yapped,
flapping its red tongue!
And there was Paddington with his sou'wester!

When I looked back,
they'd gone,
my sister and mum!

Which way? I couldn't
tell, I couldn't
see a way at all, I couldn't
go straight ahead, there was
no straight ahead, for the
cases and counters
I couldn't see over and
couldn't see round and the
hedges of blouses and
bushes of skirts,
clumps of trousers,
fences of packets of
shirts, and suddenly
mirrors
headed me this way and that till I
couldn't
remember where I'd been,
and people in all the space between
I didn't know, I'd never seen!

124

I came to a dead-end walled in mouthing tellies.
There was the lift! I got in – Going up,
said a voice, and I couldn't get out,
a fat shiny shopping bag jammed me back,
a woolly elbow caught my hat –
I saw a red coat – 'Mum!'

The wrong face looked down.

The lift stopped. Quick!
But the river of people swept me
out like a stick
into the glaring halls again,
just the same and not the same,
I didn't know where I was, or where I was
going, and people stepped into me, knocked me
as though I was nothing
and not there at all –

Then I came to a barricade
of criss-crossed racquets
with a dark lane beyond
lined with jewels like a king's hoard,
and right at the end I found
a room like a secret nobody knew,
like me.
I stood at the door.

125

Silver and gold it was, with walls
of glass where tall white dresses shone
as still as snow.
Nobody was there
but brides, they were statues,
white flowers in their hair,
smiling up at the air,
and a green chair,
arms wide,
waiting –
all waiting.
I stepped in.

The curtain like a veil flew back –
a towering lady, all in black,
came striding out!
She was looking down, with a frown
like hooks, her mouth a red
stitch pulled tight,
her thin heels
pounced on the carpet
like sewing needles
coming straight for me –
I froze. She saw me. Her
eyes were on me. She
opened her mouth –
and I ran!

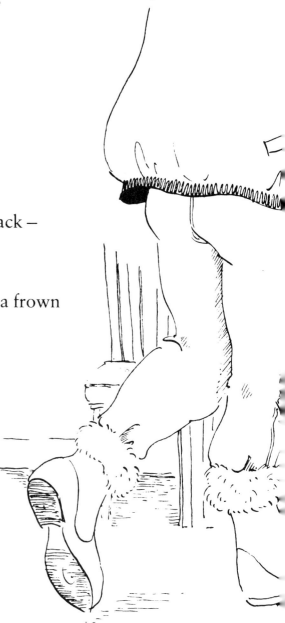

I bumped and crashed, I couldn't see,
I tripped on the roots of a silver tree,
a flurry of hats flung down with me –
I hurt my knee.

Somebody picked me up, somebody gave me a sweet,
somebody took my hand and led me to a seat.
And after a while, my mum and sister
came rushing up, looking worried and flustered
and cross. My mum said,
'Well! I'm not bringing you again!'

They hadn't bought a thing!

127

Goodbye number 5

Goodbye old flaky door
with your white and purple scars
across the wishy-washy blue,
your blisters and sorry streaks,
the peppering of nail-holes
like blackheads round a nose
and your rowdy beard of kickmarks,
and all the stories you let out and in,
the tribe of marks that signed them.

They'll scrape off, burn off, all your
skin, the new people,
if they don't chuck you first in the skip.
They'll dress you again from scratch,
smooth red perhaps like thick red
blood, smooth black or green
shiny as rubbish sacks, cheese plants
or any ad in any magazine,
and screw a brass quiff in your eye.

They'll smile at our old
neighbours, the new people:
'Would you like to come in
and see what we've done?'

And if I ever find myself again
here, old door, the way
my feet remember,
you won't know who I am.

AS I STEPPED OUT
◆ ONE MORNING ◆

The old woman and the sandwiches

I met a wizened wood-woman
Who begged a crumb of me.
Four sandwiches of ham I had:
I gave her three.

'Bless you, thank you, kindly Miss,
Shall be rewarded well –
Three everlasting gifts, whose value
None can tell.'

'Three wishes?' out I cried in glee –
'No, gifts you may not choose:
A flea and gnat to bite your back
And gravel in your shoes.'

Toad

Stop looking like a purse. How could a purse
squeeze under the rickety door and sit,
full of satisfaction, in a man's house?

You clamber towards me on your four corners –
one hand, one foot, one hand, one foot.

I love you for being a toad,
for crawling like a Japanese wrestler,
and for not being frightened.

I put you in my purse hand, not shutting it,
and set you down outside directly under
every star.

A jewel in your head? Toad,
you've put one in mine,
a tiny radiance in a dark place.

Norman Maccaig

130

It was not much, but it was something

When I am dead
I should like this to be said
above my coffin:

she would endeavour
whilst walking never
to take precedence
over an ambulance
at a zebra crossing

All change!

All change! All change!
When the guard on the train
or when the bus driver
shouts 'All change!'
and everyone has to
grab their things
in a grumbling fluster
and get out again –
just suppose
it was a magician
in disguise
playing tricks,
and in two ticks
all
the shoppers and schoolkids,
mums and dads,
with their papers and cases
and carrier bags,
grandpas, grans,
football fans,
and tourists with their maps
and their tired feet
did change –

132

and found themselves
out in the street
like a runaway zoo,
with
a bear or two,
a caribou
and a worm, perhaps –
tigers and mice,

133

a wasp,
a frog,
aardvarks,
ducks
and a kangaroo-dog,
a crocodile,
a chimpanzee –
and a few left behind on board,
a sunflower,
a couple of stones
and a
tree –

What do you think you'd be?

The dream of the cabbage caterpillars

There was no magic spell:
all of us, sleeping,
dreamt the same dream – a dream
that's ours for the keeping.

In sunbeam or dripping rain,
sister by brother
we once roamed with glee
the leaves that our mother

laid us and left us on,
browsing our fill
of green cabbage, fresh cabbage,
thick cabbage, until

134

in the hammocks we hung
from the garden wall
came sleep, and the dream
that changed us all –

we had left our soft bodies,
the munching, the crawling,
to skim through the clear air
like white petals falling!

Just so, so we woke –
so to skip high as towers,
and dip now to sweet fuel
from trembling bright flowers.

135

The dragonfly

There was once a terrible monster
lived in a pond, deep under the water.

Brown as mud he was, in the mud he hid
among murk of reed-roots, sodden twigs,
with his long hungry belly,
six legs for creeping,
eyes like headlights
awake or sleeping –
but he was not big.

A tiddler came to sneer and jeer
and flaunt his flashing tail –
Ugly old stick-in-the-mud,
couldn't catch a snail!
I'm not scared –
when, like a shot,
two pincers nab him, and he's got!

For the monster's jaw hides a clawed stalk
like the arm of a robot, a dinner fork
that's tucked away cunningly till the last minute –
shoots out – and back with a victim in it!

Days, weeks, months, two years and beyond,
fear of the monster beset the pond;
he lurked, grabbed, grappled, gobbled and grew,
ambushing always somewhere new –

Who saw him last? Does anyone know?
Don't go near the mud! But I must go!
Keep well away from the rushes! But how?
Has anyone seen my sister? Not for a week now –
she's been eaten
for certain!

And then one day, it was June, they all saw him,
he was coming slowly up out of the mud,
they stopped swimming. No one dared
approach, attack. They kept back.

Up a tall reed they saw him climbing
higher and higher, until
he broke the surface, climbing still.

137

There he stopped, in the wind and the setting sun.
We're safe at last! they cried. He's gone!

What became of the monster? Was he ill, was he sad?
Was nobody sorry? Had he crept off to die? Was he mad?

Not one of them saw how, suddenly,
as if an invisible knife had touched his back,
he has split, split completely –
his head split like a lid!

The cage is open. Slowly he comes through,
an emperor, with great eyes burning blue.

He rests then, veils of silver a cloak for him.
Night and the little stars travel the black pond.
And now, first light of the day,
his shining cloak wide wings, a flash, a whirr,
a jewelled helicopter,
he's away!

O fully he had served his time,
shunned and unlovely in the drab slime,
for freedom at the end – for the sky –
dazzling hunter, Dragonfly!

Acknowledgements

Acknowledgement is due to the following, whose permission is required for multiple reproduction:

JONI AKINRELE for her poem 'Bed!'; ANVIL PRESS for the poem 'Nursery rhyme' by Carol Ann Duffy, taken from *The Kingfisher book of comic verse*; BLOODAXE for the poem 'Bossy Parrot (my sister)' by Emma Reid, taken from *Bossy Parrot*; CHARLES CAUSLEY for his poem 'Francesco de la Vega' from *Jack the Treacle Eater*, published by Macmillan Children's Books; CHARLES CAUSLEY for the poem 'Green man in the garden' from *Collected Poems 1951–75* by Charles Causley, published by Macmillan London Ltd; CENTURY HUTCHINSON PUBLISHING for Colin West's poem 'When Betty eats spaghetti', taken from *Not to be taken seriously* published by Hutchinson; THE CIRCUS OF POETS for the poems 'No good at hobbies' and 'Hobby-horse'; COLLINS for the poem 'Grandad' by Kit Wright, taken from *Rabbiting on*; ANDRE DEUTSCH for 'Maths problems' by Alvin Schwartz, taken from *A twist of twists*; ANDRE DEUTSCH for the poem 'What's its name?' by Willard Espy, taken from *Another almanac of work at play* published by Andre Deutsch; RICHARD EDWARDS for the poems 'Walking out', 'Face to face', 'The window', 'Two of a kind' and 'Nameless'; EMI MUSIC PUBLISHING for the poem 'Lost' by James Godden, taken from *Slowly but sure* published by EMI Music; FABER for the poem 'maggie and milly and molly and may' by e e cummings, taken from *Selected poems 1923–1928*; FABER for the poem 'Some one' by Walter De La Mare, taken from *Collected poems*; FABER for the poem 'Tich Miller' by Wendy Cope, taken from *Making cocoa for Kingsley Amis*; FABER for the poem 'The Fly' by Ted Hughes, taken from *What is the truth?*; FABER for the poem 'The nose' by Ian Crichton Smith, taken from *The rattle bag*; FABER for the poem 'Who's that?' by James Kirkup, taken from *Ghosts galore*; THE FEMINIST PRESS for the poem 'Nightmare' by Siv Widerberg. Copyright © 1969, 1971 by Siv Widerberg. Translation © 1973 by Verne Moberg. From the book *I'm like me* published by The Feminist Press at the City University of New York; FONTANA YOUNG LIONS for the poems 'Horror film', 'The commentator' and 'Sally won't you walk with me?' by Gareth Owen, taken from *Song of the city*; FONTANA YOUNG LIONS for the poem 'Lies' by Kit Wright, taken from *Rabbiting on*; FONTANA YOUNG LIONS for the poems 'Our school' and 'Saturdays' by Gareth Owen, taken from *Salford Road*; GEORGE, ALLEN & UNWIN for 'Nothingmas Day' by Adrian Mitchell, taken from *Gangsters, ghosts and dragonflys*; ADAM GODDARD for the poem 'Playing with Fred'; HAMISH HAMILTON for the poem 'Listn big brodda dread, na!' by James Berry, taken from *When I dance*; HARCOURT BRACE JOVANOVICH for the poems 'Phizzog' by Carl Sandburg and 'Chinese giant' by Julie O'Callaghan, taken from *Early moon*; LIBBY HOUSTON for her poems 'All change!', 'The dragonfly', 'The dream of the cabbage caterpillars', 'It was not much, but it was something', 'Goodbye number 5', 'Like a maze' and 'The old woman and the sandwiches'; DAVID JACKSON for his poem 'Irritating sayings'; JOHN JOHNSON LTD for the poem 'Big Bert' by Richard Edwards, taken from *Whispers from a wardrobe*; JOHN JOHNSON LTD for the poem 'The flea is small' by Max Fatchen, taken from *Wry rhymes for troublesome times*; NORMAN MCCAIG for his poem 'The toad'; ORCHARD for the poem 'Taking my pen for a walk' by Julie O'Callaghan, taken from *Taking my pen for a walk*;

ORCHARD for the poems 'To pass the time' and 'The Once-a-Century-Worm'; OXFORD for the poem 'The quarrel' by Eleanor Farjeon, taken from *A first poetry book*; PAVILION BOOKS for the poem 'Pet Food' by Terry Jones, taken from *Curse of the vampire's socks*; PENGUIN for the poem 'First day at school' by Roger McGough, taken from *Strictly private*; PENGUIN for the translation by Peter Whigham of the poem 'I hate and I love' by Catullus; THE PETERS, FRASER AND DUNLOP GROUP for the poems 'Auntie and uncle' by John Hegley and 'Boasts', 'Dopey and Dozey', 'The Skyfoogle', 'My brother's on the floor roaring', 'My mum said', 'Tidy your room' and 'No one in' by Michael Rosen; PENGUIN for 'Saturday afternoon' by Peter Terson, taken from *Zigger zagger*; PUFFIN for the poems 'Fire guard', 'Pets', 'The Unincredible Hulk-in-law' and 'The leader' by Roger McGough, taken from *Sky in the pie*; PUFFIN for the poems 'Hide and seek', 'All's well that ends', 'Uncle Roger' and 'Anteater' by Roger McGough, taken from *Nailing the shadow*; PUFFIN for the poem 'You tell me' by Michael Rosen, taken from *You tell me*; PUTNAM AND GROSSET GROUP for the poem 'Wasps' by Dorothy Aldis, taken from *Anybody hungry* published by G. P. Putnam and Sons; JAY REED for his poem 'When I was small'; VIKING KESTREL for the poems 'Ever see an oyster', 'Wordfish', 'To amuse', 'I used to keep', 'A catapillow' and 'Bookworms' by Roger McGough, taken from *Imaginary menagerie*; WARD LOCK EDUCATIONAL, EAST GRINSTEAD for the poem 'All for an ice-cream' by Karen Jackson from *Ways of talking*, published by Ward Lock Educational; KEVIN WRIGHT for his poem 'The cupboard'; and finally BENJAMIN ZEPHANIAH for the poem 'Our teacher's gone crazy'.

The Publishers have made every attempt to trace the copyright holders, but in cases where they may have failed will be pleased to make the necessary arrangements at the first opportunity.